MW00794942

Bad Beanie Clique

Sketchbook

Property of

_____

If found,

please contact me by

Phone: _____

Email: _____

Find great books, journals, ebooks, and more at

Bunny17Media.com

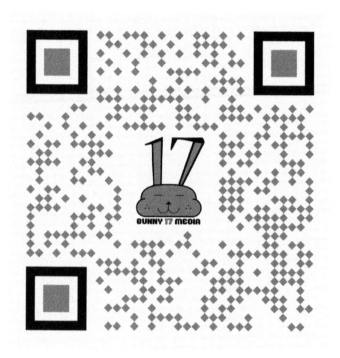

Follow @bunny17media on all social media!

CPSIA information can be obtained
at www.ICGtesting.com
Printed in the USA
LVHW081929090320
649431LV00019B/694